# DANIEL IN THE LIONS' DEN

Once, a long, long time ago, the

Jewish  were driven from their

homes and forced to live in Babylonia.

The chief city, Babylon, was filled

with s, gardens and  .

 lived there, as did a wise man

amongst the Jews,  .

Now  was troubled by dreams he did not understand.  asked his  to tell him the meaning of his dreams. "Tell us what you dreamed," said the  , "and we will tell you the meaning."

"If you cannot answer me," said  , "I will have you put to death."

The  could not tell him what he had dreamed, so  ordered his  to put all the  to death. Then  went to  and said,

"My God has shown me what your dreams mean. You dreamed of a giant  with a gold , a silver chest and arms, bronze belly and thighs, iron  and  of clay.

"You dreamed the  was broken to pieces by a  that grew into a great ."

explained that the gold

 was  ; the silver part

showed that the next kingdom would

not be as rich; bronze was for the next,

even poorer kingdom; the iron  and  of clay were for a kingdom partly strong and partly weak, which would be split into two; "and the rock, which finally breaks the  into pieces, is God's everlasting kingdom."

 was so grateful for 's explanation that he made him leader

of his  and gave him many gifts

of gold chains and fine horses.

Some time after,  had a great

gold  made. He ordered the

 to bow down to it or be

thrown into a fiery . Three

Jews, , refused, saying, "Our

God will save us from death."

 was angry and told his

to throw  into the .

God sent to  an , who

fanned the flames out of the  to

kill the , leaving the three Jews

unharmed.

"Your God is great!" cried  .

After  died, his son

ruled over Babylon.  held a

great feast in his  . Everyone

drank wine from silver  , then

 brought out the gold

stolen from the Temple in Jerusalem.

Suddenly a  appeared and

wrote some unknown words on the

wall. Everyone was afraid and

called for  to explain them.

When  saw the writing on the wall, he told , "The words mean that God is angry with you for using the gold  from his temple. You will not be king of Babylon for long. Soon its s, gardens and  will belong to a new king."

That night, enemy  killed him.

The new king of Babylon was . He was fond of  and kept him as one of his .  was by then an old man, but  was pleased with his work. The other  who served  were jealous of . They plotted to ruin him through his love of God.

Then the  advised  to make a new law. "You are so great; command the  to say prayers in future only to you."

When  heard about the new law, he knew at once that the  were trying to get him into trouble.  said his prayers at his open  three times a day. 's new law was not going to change 's ways. When the  saw that  was still praying to God, they

told , who sent his  to

arrest  .

The  brought  to the

palace.  said, "Obey my laws

and I will let you go."

"I must first obey God's laws," said

 . "I cannot pray to you,  ."

"May your God save you," said

 . Then he told his  to put

 into a cave full of hungry

 and close the entrance with a

great . There  was left.

Next morning,  looked into

the cave and was amazed that

was still alive amongst the  .

"The  did me no harm. My

God closed their mouths," said  .

Then  said, "Your God is the

greatest. I will order all the  of

Babylon to respect him."